SONATA in A, K.331/300i

This much-played sonata should not be approached lightly as a hackneyed or 'easy' work. Its popularity owes as much to the warmth of the opening theme and the trio of the minuet as to the obvious appeal of the final *Alla Turca*. It calls for spontaneity, which the player should never confuse with irresponsibility. None of the movements is in sonata form, unless we regard the Minuet and the Trio as each representing sonata form in miniature, and the predominance of A major and minor sets a challenge, which Mozart met by offering a wide range of textures, and not only in the opening variations. They include effects of pastiche, even of caricature, and call for warmth of heart as well as humour. There are relics of a harpsichord style in the crossed-hands doublings, and in the sharp contrasts of *piano* and *forte*, which should not be ironed out by pianistic crescendos. Some early fortepianos had a percussion stop to add realism to the drum-and-cymbals tuttis of the finale. Mozart wrote other mock-Turkish music, including the well-known overture to *Die Entführung* ('The Seraglio'). The Turkish episode in the Rondo of the A major Violin Concerto, K.219, is less extravagantly scored, but a more useful parallel in its alternation of fiddler's gymnastics with humorously square tuttis. The key of A minor was natural to the violin, and the association remained.

1   The movement is a long one if all the repeats are observed, and some players play havoc with the form by picking and choosing. The only possible alternative to 'all or none' is to observe the repeats in the theme and the final variation, which will sound abrupt without them. The tempo of the theme is best judged by thinking ahead to the detail of variations 1 and 2, which should flow naturally in its wake. It lies on the elusive border between two and six beats per bar, and though the theme is song-like it has the gentle lilt of a siciliano. In the opening figure only two notes, not three, are slurred and this phrasing naturally affects the bass-line too. Pianists who think this effect fussy should ask a violinist to demonstrate the difference. Any suspicion of a double-dot will spoil the dignity of the theme, and in general the upbeats need to be light in order to give point to Mozart's sforzatos in b.4, etc. Imagine D major chords at these points and then underline Mozart's B minor harmony as requested. Note the change of texture at b.9, where the left hand becomes pure accompaniment, and the sense of fulfilment in the concluding *forte* phrase (bb.17–18). The small notes at the end of b.17 and the octave descent should still be singable when they recur at the end of variation 1. Note also a parallel in the closing bars of the Minuet.

Most of the variations adopt a different dynamic contrast in their first halves: four bars of *piano* answered by four of *forte* in a new texture. Not, however, in the original edition, variation 4; and, in keeping with its character, the *fortes* in variation 5, at bb.95–6, are only token ones. A problem in variation 1 is that the slender dissonant notes – B♯, D♯, etc – are unsupported but carry the main beats. It is better to exaggerate rather than neglect the short slurs, and the l.h. off-beat chords need touching in lightly. Beware of crushing the l.h. grace-notes in variation 2. The briefest breathing-space is

needed before variation 3, ⸱ key frame of mind, and tl legato of a fine oboist, even octaves (where a continuing legato is implied). The to the major (variation 4) follows effortlessly, with the crossing quavers thought of as 'vocal leaps' and not pedalled through. The adagio variation needs 'placing' and its florid decoration suggests a tempo at least twice as slow as the original theme. Bars 103–4 are the touchstone: the fifth-beat interpolations lose their magic if there is no time to observe Mozart's infinitesimal, but meticulous, rests. The final allegro variation is brilliant in *forte*, with a foretaste of the spread l.h. chords of the *Alla Turca*, but light-fingered in *piano*. Think in a brisk four-in-a-bar rather than two: the rapid turns in bb.128–30 need lively accents to balance the l.h. chords.

2   The rhythmic poise of the Minuet, like that of the first variation, is elusive and often lost from the start. If the octave A in b.2 sounds like a down-beat the illusion will carry on into b.4, and, as before, it is a lesser evil to over-accent first beats in practising until the pulse is grasped. The Minuet itself suggests a wind-band, with horns marking the outline of the opening bars, and some of the florid runs (e.g. from b.11) given to clarinets. The tempo is ceremonial, with the regularity of a dance-movement. Many editions supply naturals in bb.24–6, but the mixture of A major and minor may have been intentional. Avoid fussy dynamics and echo-effects in the Trio (D major). It is wholly melodic and long-flowing, and the l.h. crossings will make their own subtle changes of colour, like flute-tone added to strings, with the gentlest humour when they turn into bird-song in bb.57 & 93. The double octaves (bb.68–72) are unusual for Mozart, and the *forte* is best self-contained, with the notes even and slightly detached, again as in a wind serenade. No extra pause before or after the Trio.

3   The four-squareness of the *Alla Turca* is essential to its character and it benefits from being played with a sense of humour. The form is not the simple rondo but ABCBAB plus coda, with B as the refrain in which the imaginary drums and cymbals join. The A minor theme, and the F sharp minor episode, never approach this *forte*: the *f* in bb.20 & 84 is a purely local event to mark the shock of an unexpected harmonic twist. Spontaneous shading, however, should not be ruled out. The move to C major after the first double-bar calls for a slight lift, with a drop at the return to A minor; but no artist will repeat it photographically. The A major refrain requires both crispness and resonance, but the l.h. spread chords should not resound through the bar, though more pedal may be allowed in the coda where the r.h. 'cymbal clashes' come thick and fast (e.g. b.101). The sudden drop to *p* halfway through b.109 is a 'terraced' dynamic, so therefore make no crescendo into b.116. Not all players and teachers will agree with the fingerings suggested throughout the sonata, and it would be impossible to indicate the countless tolerable alternatives. Some recommended ones, e.g. the r.h. in bb.1–2 and b.12 of the Minuet, will help phrasing and accentuation; and the

tradition of changing fingers on repeated-note figures as a matter of course has not been followed. In a moderate tempo it can lead to fussiness as in variation 5 of the first movement – l.h. bb.95–6, r.h. b.97 – where a gentle hand-touch is all that is needed.

D.M.

TEXTUAL NOTES

Composition   Munich or Vienna, 1781–3

Sources   autograph, final leaf only (finale, bars 90–end; remainder lost), from collection of Antonio de Almeida, Lisbon [A]; first edition, as no.2 of *Trois sonates pour le clavecin ou pianoforte composèes par W.A. Mozart. Oeuvre VI* (Vienna: Artaria, 1784) (nos.1 and 3 are K.330/300*h* and 332/300*k*) [E]

Notes   The text, inevitably, follows E; any changes are noted below. The exemplar used, from the collection of Dr Alan Tyson, is of the very rare first impression (not to my knowledge used hitherto in an edition of these sonatas); many of the printing plates were evidently damaged and were replaced for later impressions by freshly engraved ones, which have several errors and omissions. For the sonata's final bars, A is an additional source; as in the preceding and following sonatas, the RH in A is notated in the soprano clef (also the LH, bb.110–15).

1st movt
bar

2	RH slur covers 3 notes; all the others clearly cover only 2
64	LH *1* slur
95	*1* q
95–6	last q beat notated 2 dsq, sq, sq rest
105	RH *13* originally not stacc., *14–18* stacc. dots, cf. 97
106	RH *10 d″*, usually changed to *b′* by analogy with theme and other variations, but possibly correct; *f* and *p* are placed below staff but probably apply to both hands
108	
(2nd)	LH *a*, dot missing
112	LH *e*, dot missing
113	LH 1st chord: usual reading, an octave lower, is in error, deriving from wrong re-engraving of a damaged plate; the earliest print is clearly as shown

2nd movt
bar

2–3	RH slurring ambiguous: 2 has *1–3* or *1–4*, 3 has *2–4*; 32 has *1–3*, 33 has *1–4* or *2–4*
18	LH *e′* missing
19	dynamic mark *p*, surely in error for *f*
24–6	this passage is commonly shown in A minor, but the accidentals in E are reproduced here exactly as they appear (it is impossible to be sure of Mozart's intentions, and pianists preferring the traditional reading should play all C's ♮ in these bars)
25	'cres:' seemingly engraved here, then obliterated
28	LH dots missing
32–3	see 2–3
36–8	LH all one slur; cf. 6–8
81	lower LH notes printed a 3rd low

3rd movt tempo given as 'Allgrino'
bar

122	A, 1st chord *c″♯* and *a″* only
125	E, last q *c″♯–c‴♯*
126	E, 2nd crotchet LH bottom note missing

Mozart

Sonata in A

FOR PIANO

K. 331

Edited by STANLEY SADIE

Fingering and performance
notes by DENIS MATTHEWS

The Associated Board of
the Royal Schools of Music

Abbreviations in Textual Notes

cf. – *confer* [compare]; dsq – demisemiquaver; edn – edition; K – no. in Köchel catalogue of Mozart's works (no. before / is original no., no. after is that in 6th edn, 1964); LH – left hand; movt – movement; q – quaver; RH – right hand; sq – semiquaver; stacc. – staccato

Pitch – *c'* is middle C, *d'* the note above, *b* the note below; *c''* and *c'''* one and two octaves above, *c, C* and *C'* one, two and three octaves below

Numerals – arabic numerals in roman normally denote bar nos.; arabic in italic denote note nos. within the bar, counting left to right, chords downwards, and including all grace notes as notated

Editorial notes

In the printing of the text a distinction has been made between original and editorial markings. Slurs and ties added editorially are indicated by a small perpendicular stroke; editorial staccato marks (whether dots or wedges), dynamic markings and accidentals are indicated by the use of smaller type.

Editorial realizations of ornaments are shown in small notes above the text at the first occurrence of the ornament concerned in each movement. These realizations are based on the leading sources contemporary with Mozart, such as C. P. E. Bach's *Versuch über das wahre Art das Clavier zu spielen* (1753–62), Leopold Mozart's *Versuch einer gründlichen Violinschule* (1756) and Daniel Gottlob Türk's *Clavierschule* (1789). Our suggestions should not be taken as mandatory; any proper realization must take account of the tempo chosen for the movement concerned and the player's capabilities, and in a trill a player should feel free to play more notes, or fewer, as seems right. No ornament that feels awkward to the player, or sounds clumsy, is being satisfactorily realized. A player who wants to vary the realization of ornaments more extensively, however, would be well advised first to consult the writings of contemporary authorities, or failing that a summary of their views in a good modern reference work; he should note that except in very rare circumstances a trill should begin on the upper note in music of this period.

SONATA in A

K.331/300*i* (*c.*1781)

Andante grazioso

Var. 1

Var. 2

Var. 5
Adagio

Var. 6
Allegro

MENUETTO

* possibly all C's should be ♮ in bars 24-6; see Textual Notes.

18

[Menuetto D.C.]

ALLA TURCA
Allegretto